THE MANATEE WHO FINDS MINDFULNESS

WRITTEN BY ALYSON MURPHY

ILLUSTRATED BY BETSY DOUGLASS

indiepen

IndiePen, a Vedere Press Company

The Manatee Who Finds Mindfulness
Copyright ©2018 by Alyson Murphy
Illustrations by Betsy Douglass

ISBN-13: 978-1-7329886-2-0
ISBN-10: 1-7329886-2-5

To the Powells and to the Stevensons:

Once a nanny, always a friend,

Wishing you loving kindness until the end.

Macy loves swimming in the warm, shallow sea,

next to her mother where she's safe and carefree.

Her paddle-like tail helps

her move smooth and slow,

but flipping it fast makes

her speed up and GO!

"Slow down!" calls her mother. "Stop, look, and listen!"

But Macy darts off-she sees something glisten!

She chases silver fish

with shimmering scales

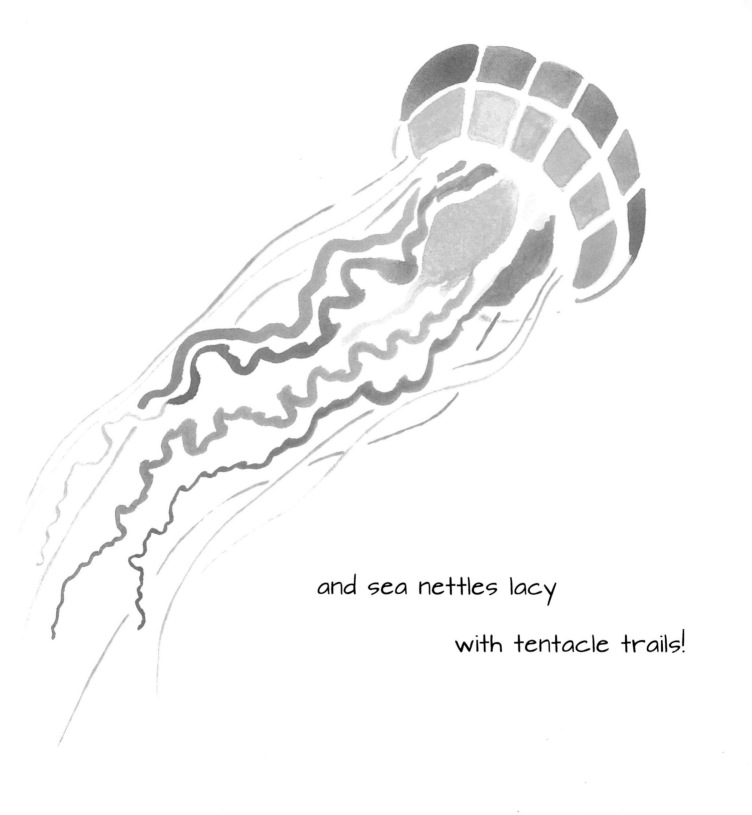

and sea nettles lacy

with tentacle trails!

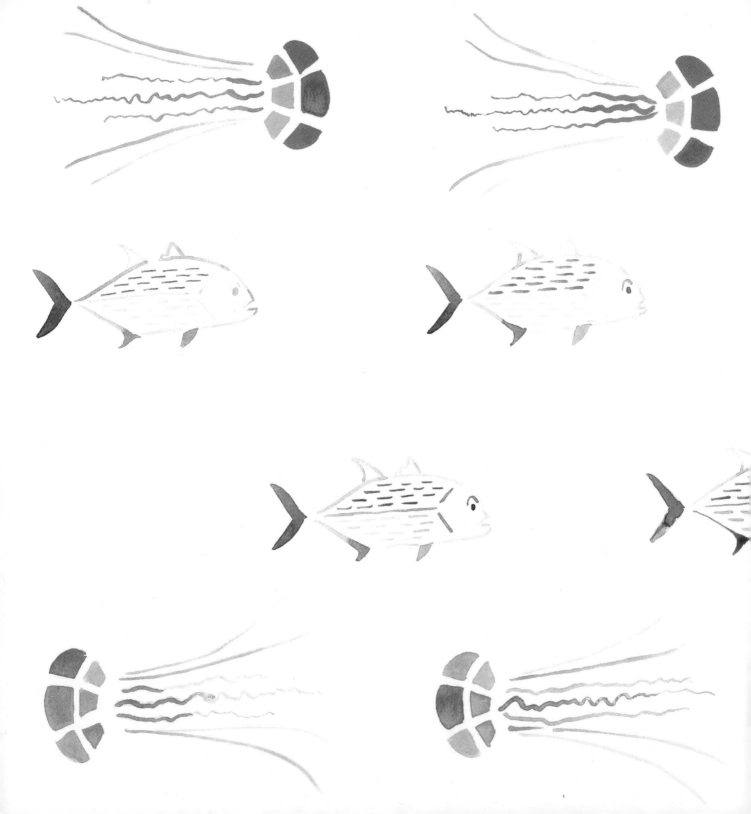

They float along currents, pulsing as they go.

Macy's never seen such a beautiful show.

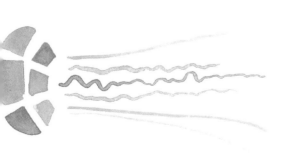

"So pretty!" she says, as she reaches out to touch.

ZAP! It stings her flipper!
OUCH! It hurts so much!

"Mama!" cries Macy. "I'm stung and so afraid."

Please come find me quickly! I'm sorry I strayed!"

Macy's heart beats wildly. She has lost her way!

"Stop, look, and listen! That's what my mom would say."

Macy lays as still as stone on the ocean floor

She sees a sea star crawling- Wait! There goes one more!

"I'll concentrate on counting them, One...Two...Three...

And bring my attention to each thing I see:

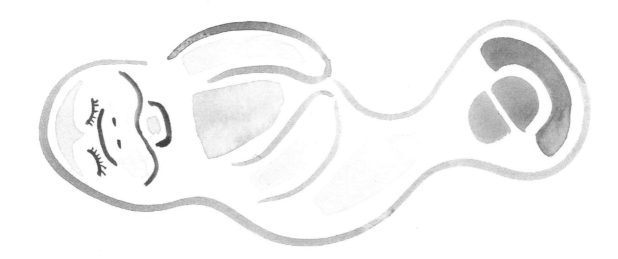

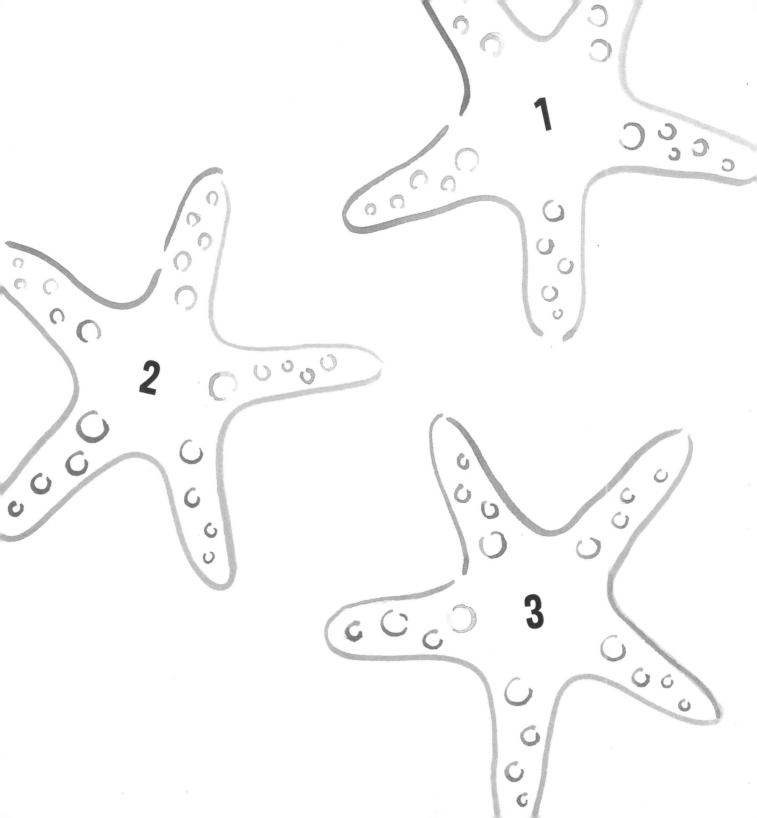

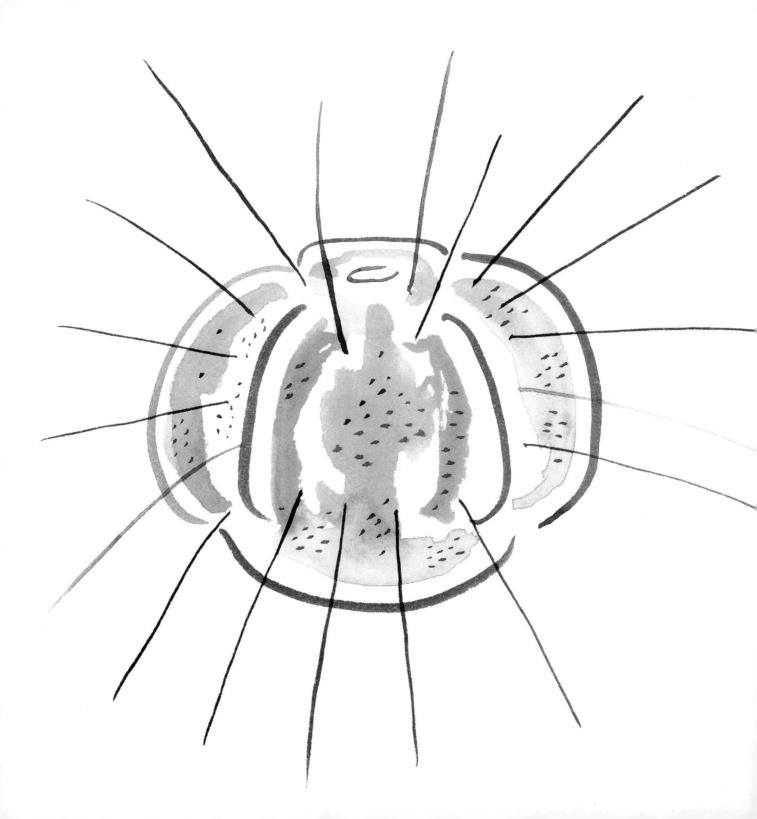

A spiky sea urchin!
An elegant stingray!"

Macy finds her worries
start to float away.

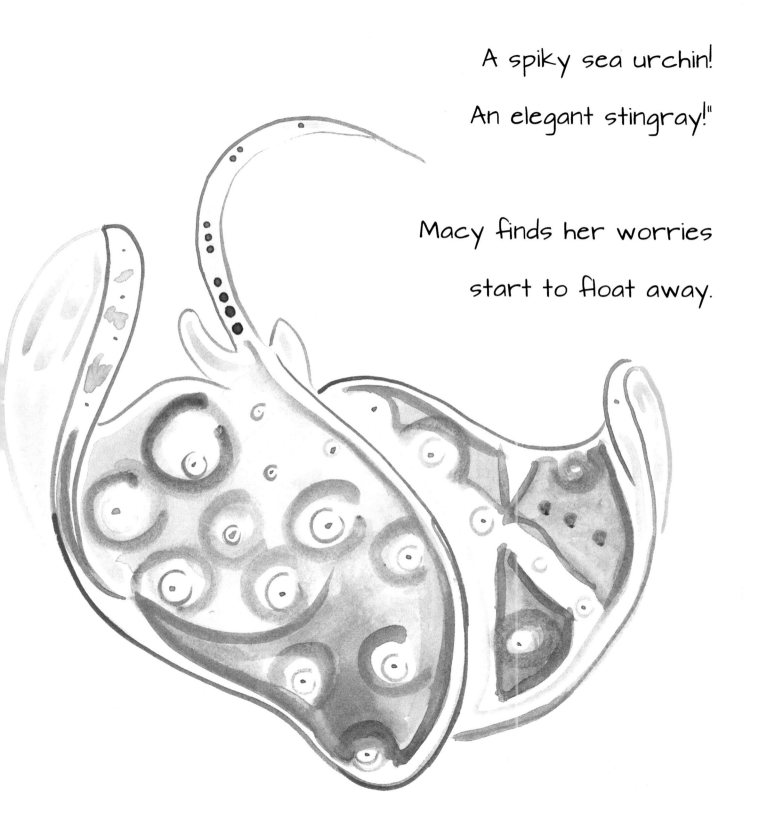

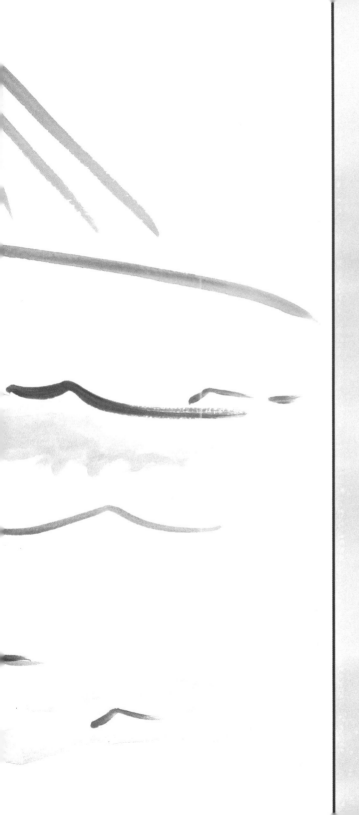

She rises to the surface.

It's choppy there!

Then she sinks below,
after deep breaths of air.

Her thoughts start to settle, and her mind is clear.

She lies still and listens. What does she hear?

The swishing tails of fish
and crab legs crawling.

Then through the murky sea,
she hears...

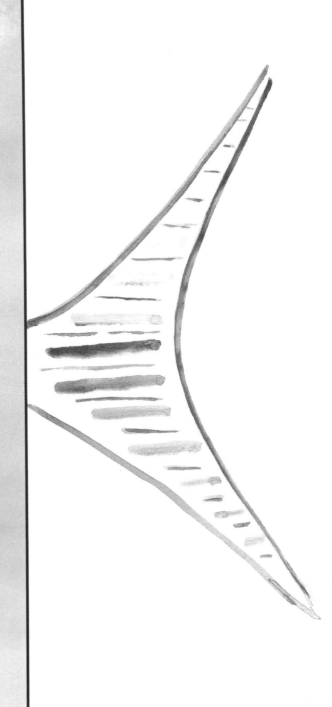

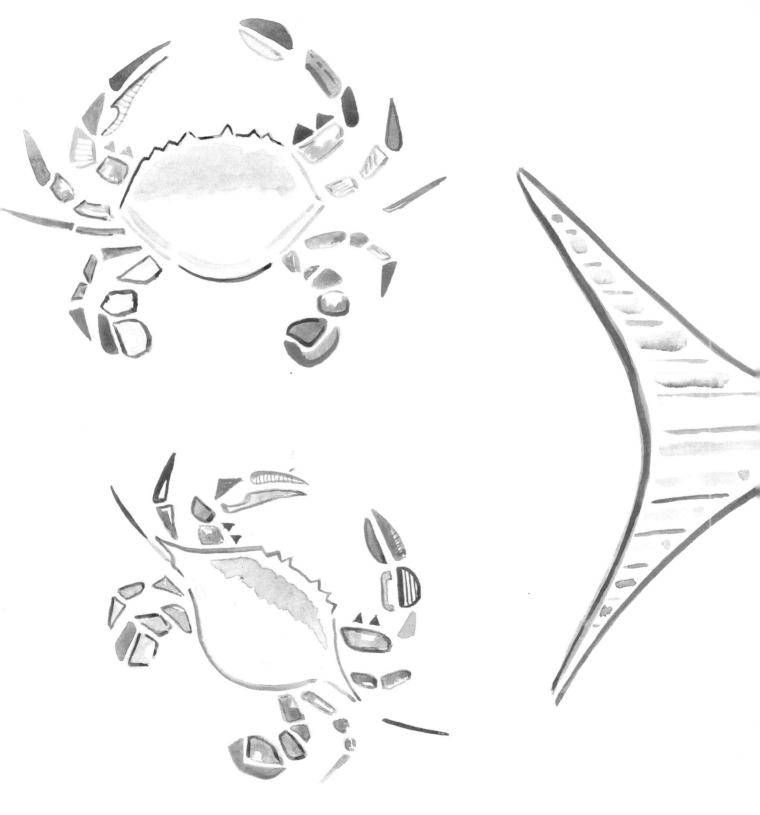

her mother calling!

"Maaaaaaaacyyyyyyyy!"

"Maaaammmmmaaaaa!"

"I was so worried something happened to you!"

"I'm sorry," said Macy. "I was worried too.

My thoughts were as choppy

as waves on the surface,

so I used mindful moments

to focus with purpose.

And no matter how murky

the waves appeared,

I found stillness within me

that was calm and clear."

"I'm glad you are safe and you found your way home.

Peace is never far away, no matter where you roam.

If you ever feel lost, either within or at sea,

Remember peace lives inside us all, within you and within me."

A BEGINNERS GUIDE FOR MINDFUL MEDITATION

Mindfulness can be found in every culture since the beginning of history. If practiced correctly, the benefits include our ability to increase self-control, focus and compassion and decrease stress, anxiety and judgement. We can increase mindful behavior through digital detoxing, reading, yoga, exercise, music, coloring, mindful dining, breathing techniques and meditation. While all these activities will help increase focus and well-being, only meditation can help us manifest divine inner peace with no cost at all.

I like to introduce all my beginner classes to meditation with Metta Meditation
which translates as "loving kindness".

Just follow along these three simple steps in a comfortable position (eyes closed)
and either use my metta meditation or make up your own.

STEP ONE: Start with directing 3 or 4 phrases of kindness and compassion towards yourself

May I be happy and healthy
May I be peaceful
May I live at ease and with kindness

STEP TWO: After a week of meditating on ourselves, add in somebody that you love and care for.
Sometimes you can even choose someone that might be hard to love or care for.

May you be happy and healthy
May you be peaceful
May you live at ease and with kindness

STEP THREE: Finally, include a larger selection of people whether everyone in
your community, county, country or even the world.

May all beings be happy and healthy
May all beings be peaceful
May all beings live at ease and with kindness

At the end of every metta meditation, finish by tapping your thumb to each figure while stating the words
PEACE (thumb to pointer finger) BEGINS (thumb to middle finger) WITH (thumb to ring finger)

ME (thumb to pinky). NAMASTE

ABOUT THE AUTHOR

ALYSON MURPHY received a Bachelor of Arts in Mass Communications from the University of South Carolina and holds certifications in professional etiquette and advanced behavior analysis from the Charleston School of Protocol and the Nonverbal Group in Manhattan. She currently teaches classes at a number of the Charleston County Schools that are heavily based on social psychology and mindfulness, helping bridge the gap between the rules of etiquette and the principles they are founded on. For more information or to inquire about a school presentation on manners or mindfulness, please visit www.murphysmanners.com.

ABOUT THE ILLUSTRATOR

A native of Raleigh, North Carolina, BETSY DOUGLASS began her artistic talents while studying under Kim Stewart at the age of nine. Betsy's art career blossomed over the years as she often painted commissions for friends and family. During her time at UNCW, Betsy painted works for several establishments in Wilmington and Wrightsville Beach, North Carolina. Betsy now lives and works from her studio in Charleston, SC.

Made in the USA
Columbia, SC
20 November 2019